GREAT ESCAPE MAZES

Roger Moreau

Sterling Publishing Co., Inc.
New York

10 9 8 7 6 5 4 3 2 1

Published by Sterling Publishing Company, Inc.
387 Park Avenue South, New York, N.Y. 10016
© 1999 by Roger Moreau
Distributed in Canada by Sterling Publishing
C/o Canadian Manda Group,One Atlantic Avenue, Suite 105
Toronto, Ontario, Canada M6K 3E7
Distributed in Great Britain and Europe by Cassell PLC
Wellington House, 125 Strand, London WC2R 0BB, England
Distributed in Australia by Capricorn Link (Australia) Pty Ltd.
P.O. Box 6651, Baulkham Hills, Business Centre, NSW 2153, Australia
Manufactured in the United States of America

Sterling ISBN 0-8069-7098-7

CONTENTS

A NOTE ON THE SUGGESTED USE OF THIS BOOK

As you work your way through the pages of this book, try not to mark them. This will enable you to find the escape routes over and over again and will give your friends a chance to find the escape routes without showing them the ones you took.

SPECIAL WARNING: If the escape appears too difficult, avoid the temptation to start at the end and work your way backwards. This technique would be a violation of the rules and could result in a severe reprimand.

COVER MAZE: Find your way to safety from the sinking *Titanic* by descending the rope to the ice floe below. Without falling into the sea, find your way to the over-turned lifeboat.

INTRODUCTION

There are many kinds of escape. You could be held captive in prison against your will or trapped by enemy forces. You could be at the mercy of nature or a hostile environment through accident or misadventure. Often death will be the ultimate penalty, unless you can escape through your own efforts or are rescued by others. An escape or rescue from any of these circumstances always involves courage, risk and danger.

Throughout history, there have been many great escapes, and some of the greatest occurred during the twentieth century. Thanks to historians, photographers and the media, most of them have been well documented and details can be found in books and libraries. You will learn about some of these escapes here, and you will even have a chance to be involved in the rescues and experience the difficulties of the escape that took place. Hopefully, you will be successful and have the same kind of determination and courage that those involved in the real escapes had. It is also hoped that the day will never come when you will find yourself in a situation where you will really have to escape.

Now turn this page and go forth to be a part of some of the greatest escapes of the twentieth century.

The *Endurance* Is Trapped in the Ice

In 1915 on their way to Antarctica, Ernest Shackleton and the crew of the *Endurance* got trapped in pack ice. Help them make their way through the ice to Elephant Island.

Go for Help for the Stranded Crew

Shackleton and four companions sailed 800 miles to South Georgia Island for help, but landed on the wrong side. Find a clear path over the island to the whaling station.

Rescue Shackleton's Men

In August 1916, on his fourth attempt, Shackleton finally led a Chilean ship, the

Yelcho, back to their camp on Elephant Island to save the rest of his trapped crew. Miraculously, all had survived the winter. Find a path through the ice so the steamer can rescue Shackleton's men.

Crash of the *Italia*

In 1928, Umberto Nobile attempted to fly over the north pole in the semi-rigid

START

SET UP
RED TENT AND
CAMP HERE

Italia, but high winds broke the airship apart and the gondola crashed onto the ice. The survivors set up the famous "red tent" in the hope that it would be seen easily by rescuers. Find your way from the crash and set up the red tent.

Search for the Red Tent

Several attempts were made to locate the wreck, including one fatal one. Roald

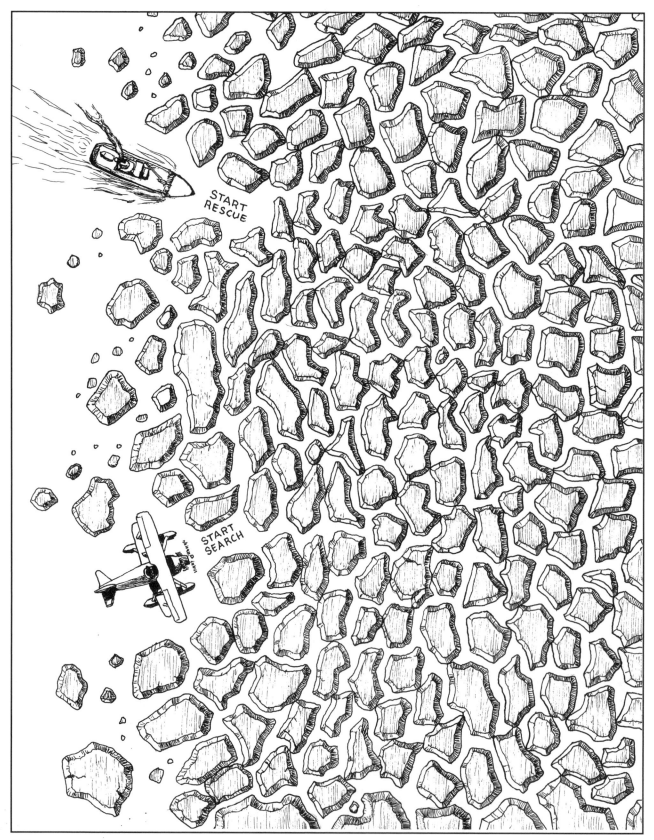

Amundsen, who had flown over the pole with Nobile in 1926, went down and was never heard from. Use the seaplane to search for Nobile and his men in the red tent. When you find them, sail the ship in through the ice for the rescue.

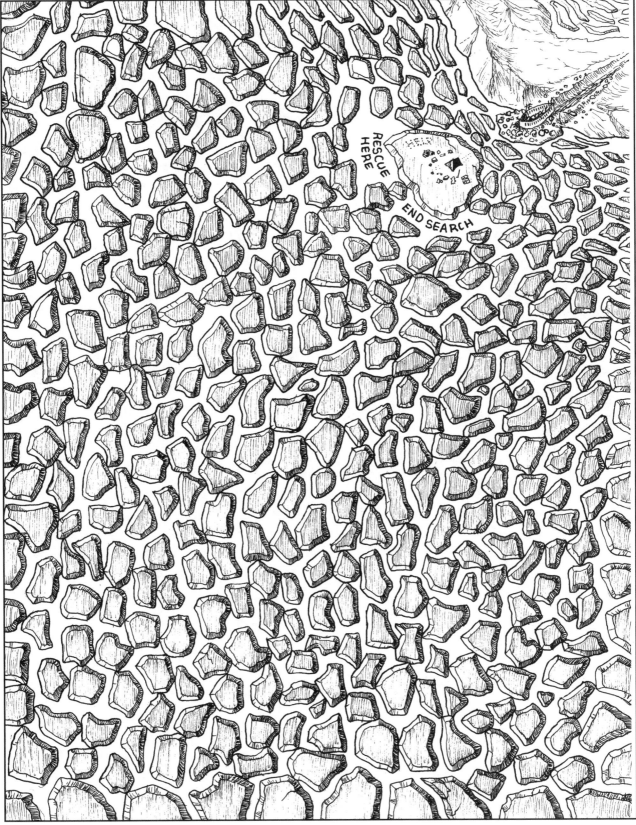

The *Hindenburg* Explodes

In May 1936, the *Hindenburg* airship, filled with hydrogen, caught fire as it was

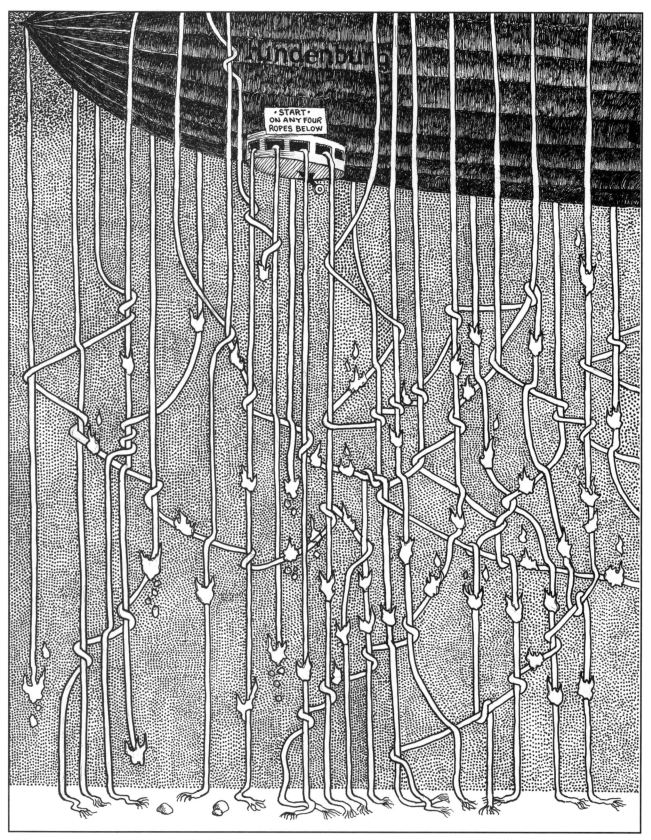

landing in New Jersey at the end of its maiden voyage. Escape the exploding airship by climbing down the ropes from the gondola. You can move from rope to
rope where they touch, but avoid spots where the rope is burning. Hurry!

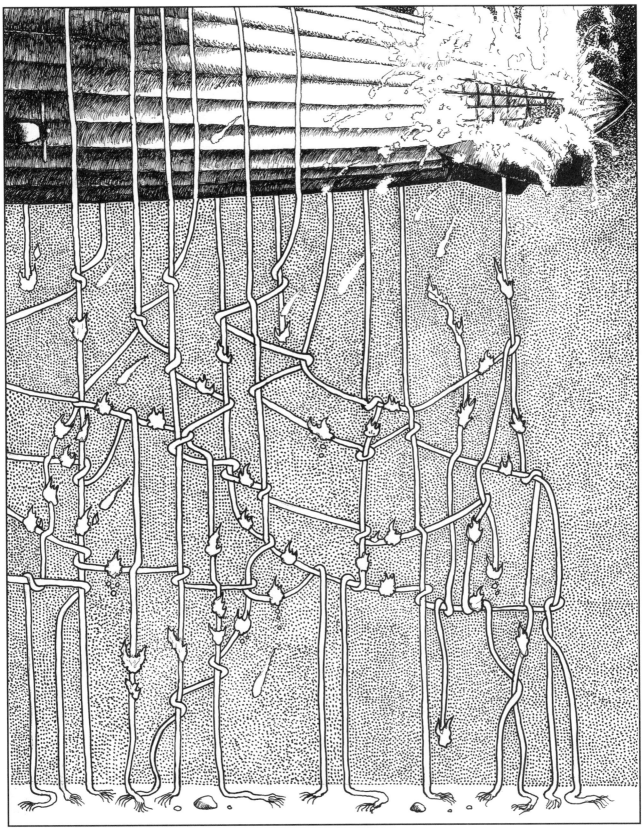

The *Squalus* Is Down

In 1939, when the U.S. submarine *Squalus* sank during testing in 240 feet of water

START

in Portsmouth, New Hampshire, harbor, she had over 50 men trapped in her hull. An experimental rescue diving bell was sent to the scene. Can you help guide the bell to the sub. Watch out for the school of cod that are swimming by.

Escape from Dunkirk

In 1940, nearly 400,000 Allied troops were trapped on the beach at Dunkirk in France

by advancing German forces and bombarded with heavy fire from the German air force. Most were evacuated by a huge flotilla of military, commercial, fishing, and pleasure boats. Help the troops find a clear path to the boats on the beach.

We Must Sink the *Bismarck*

Help the *Ark Royal*'s biplanes find the German battleship *Bismarck* for a torpedo run. Next, guide shells from the *Repulse*, *Rodney* and *King George V* to sink the ship.

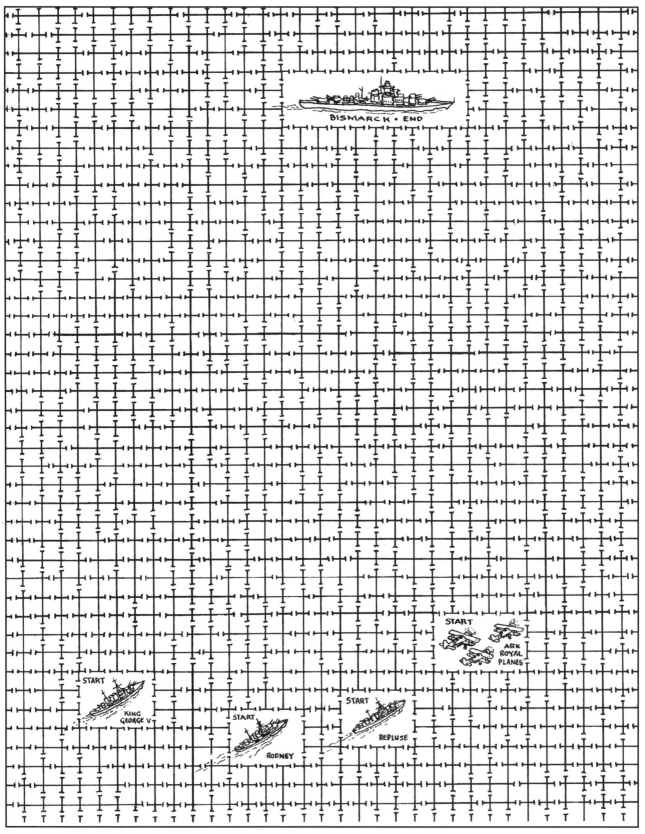

Doolittle's Raiders Down Behind Enemy Lines

After a bombing raid on Japan early in 1940, Doolittle's B-25 bombers had to ditch in occupied China. Help the fliers find a path to freedom. Do not pass a Japanese flag.

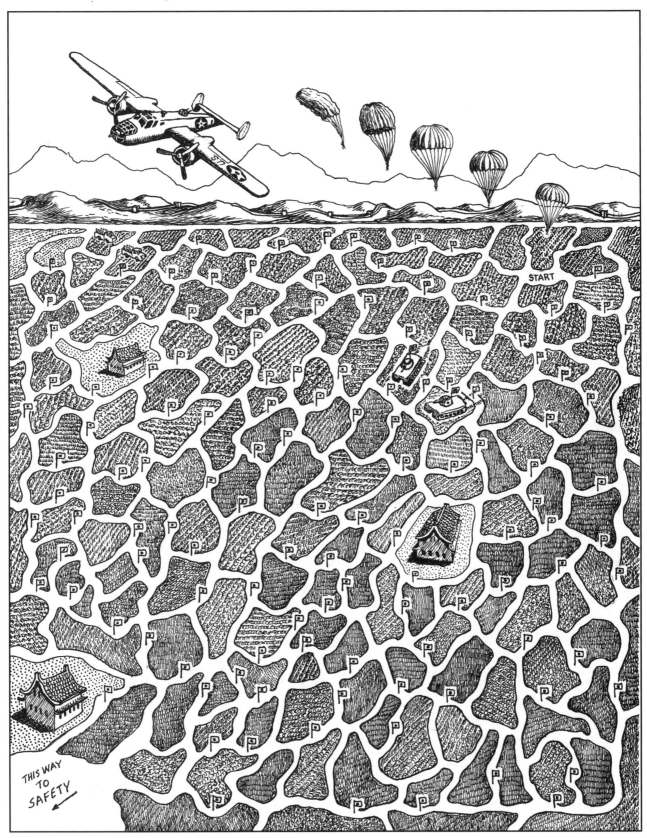

The Great Escape

One of the greatest escapes of World War II was from the German prisoner-of-war

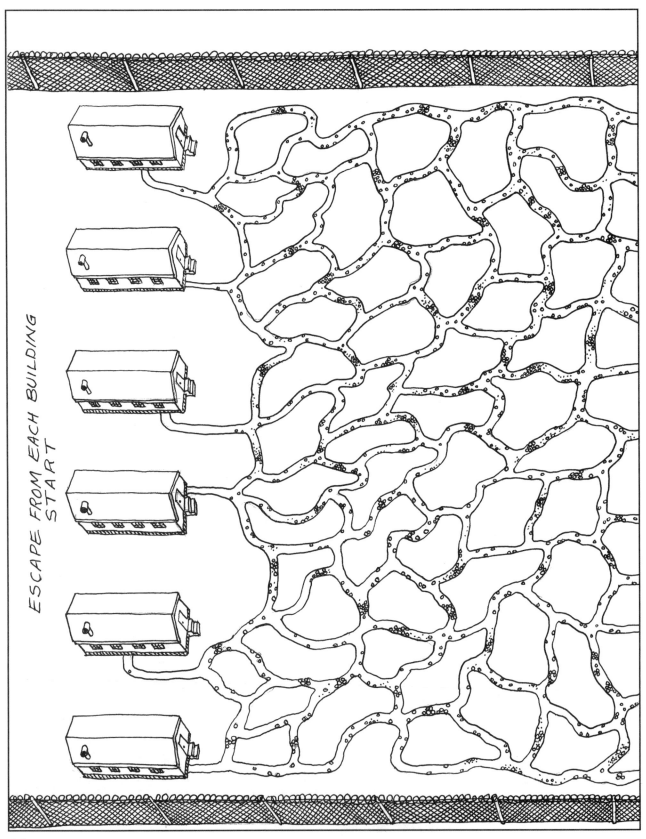

ESCAPE FROM EACH BUILDING
START

camp Stalag Luft III. For months, captured airmen dug several tunnels from their prisoner's barracks to the outside beyond the fence. Help the men escape from each building by finding a clear tunnel passage.

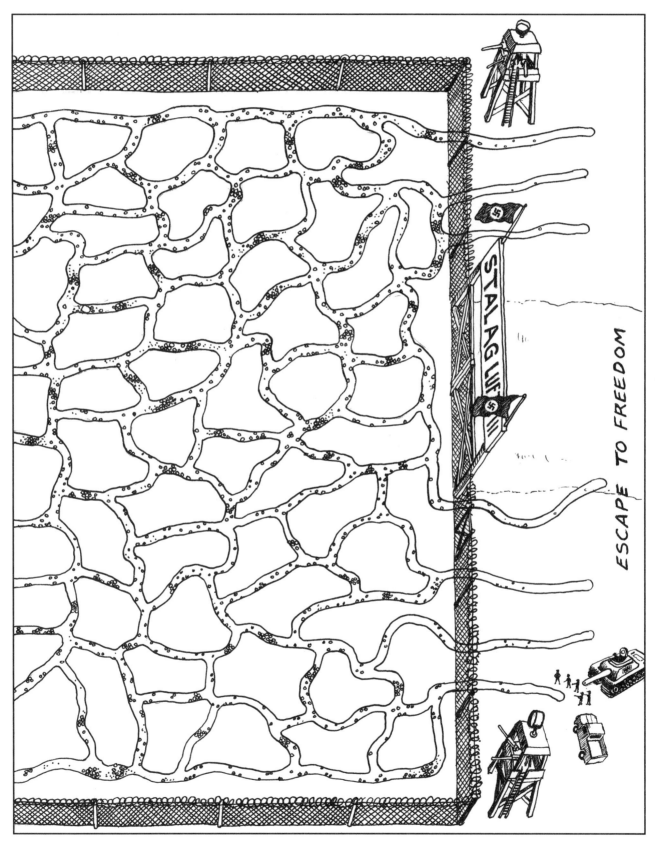

Escape from Sobibor

Sobibor was a German concentration camp in Poland. In 1943, over 300 Jewish

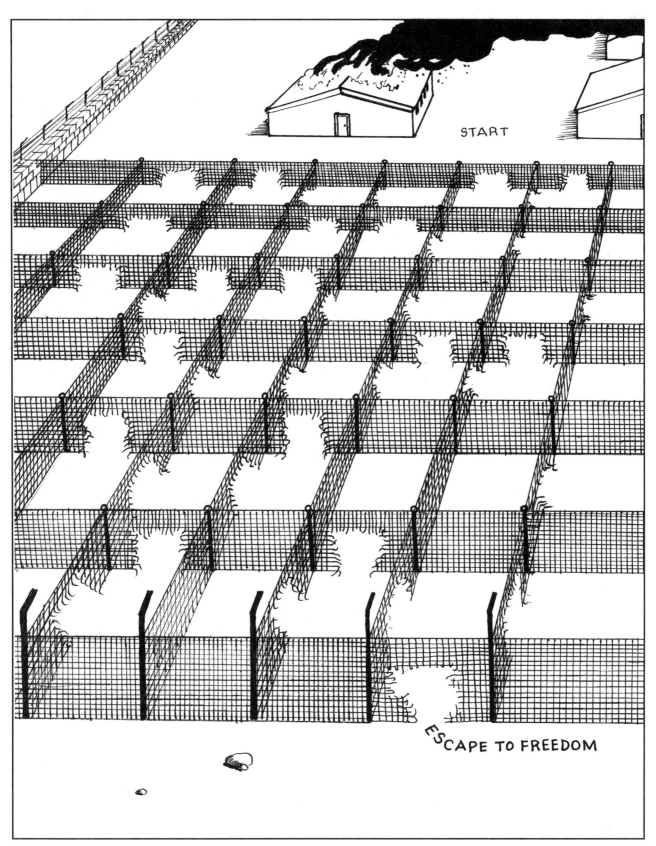

START

ESCAPE TO FREEDOM

prisoners made a daring escape from this death camp. As a result, Heinrich Himmler ordered the camp closed and destroyed. Help the escapees find their way through the holes in the fences to freedom.

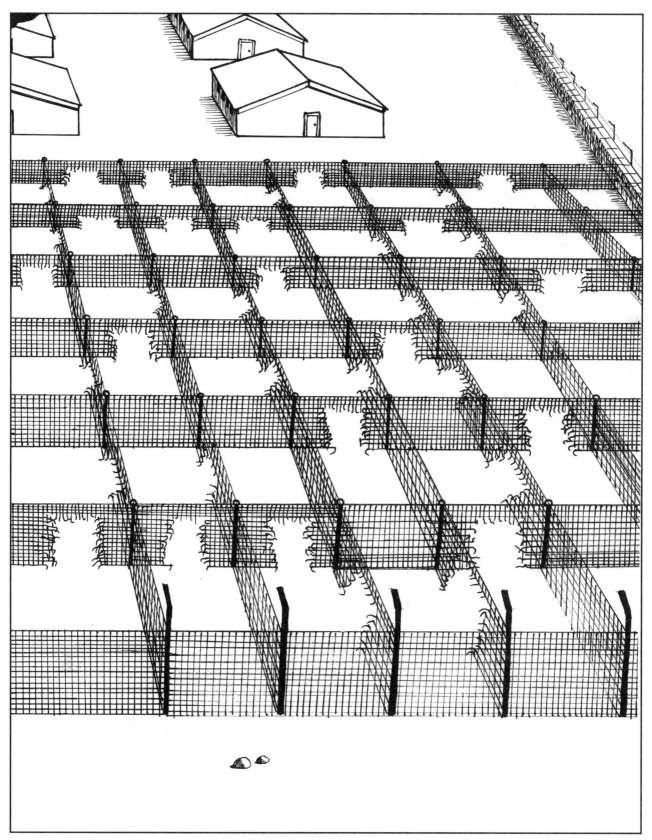

MacArthur Must Flee Corregidor

In 1942, the invading Japanese were advancing on Corregidor, an island fortress

off the Bataan Peninsula at the entrance to Manila bay. It was important to get General Douglas MacArthur safely to the southern Philippines on a PT boat. Help the boat find a safe course through the dangerous currents.

Escape Under the Ocean

During World War II, many submarines had to escape terrifying enemy attacks.

This submarine has just made a successful torpedo attack and is trying to get away. Help the sub finds its way through the exploding depth charges and escape to safety.

Escape of the Dalai Lama

Chinese Communist troops are storming up the steps of the Dalai Lama's summer

palace in Lhasa. He must escape to set up a new Tibetan government in exile. Help him move up and down the ropes and along the paths to freedom.

ESCAPE TO SAFETY →

"Houston, We Have a Problem"

Apollo 13 suffered severe damage on its way to the moon in 1970, and the crew

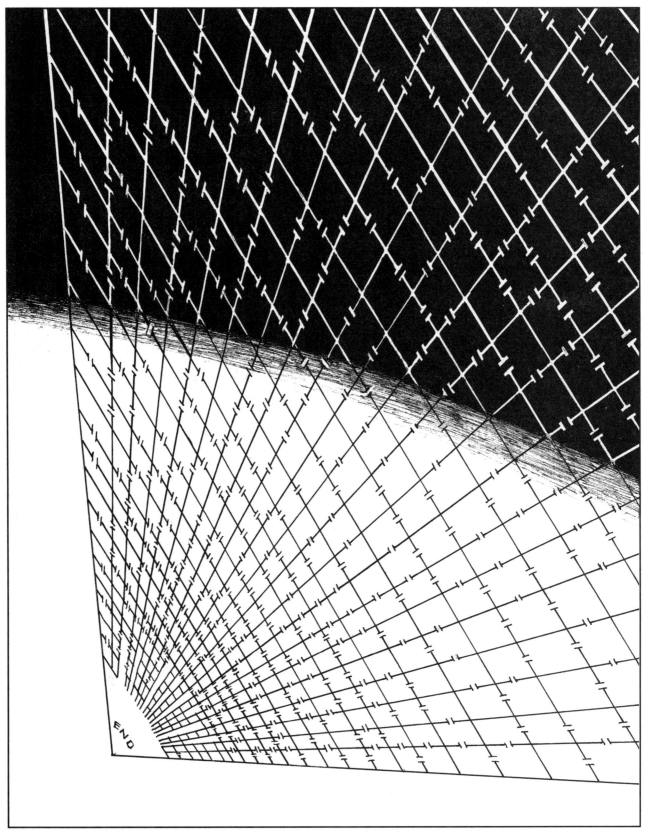

had to shut down the service module. They moved into the lunar module and had to conserve oxygen and fuel for nearly six and a half days. Help them find their way home by moving through the gaps.

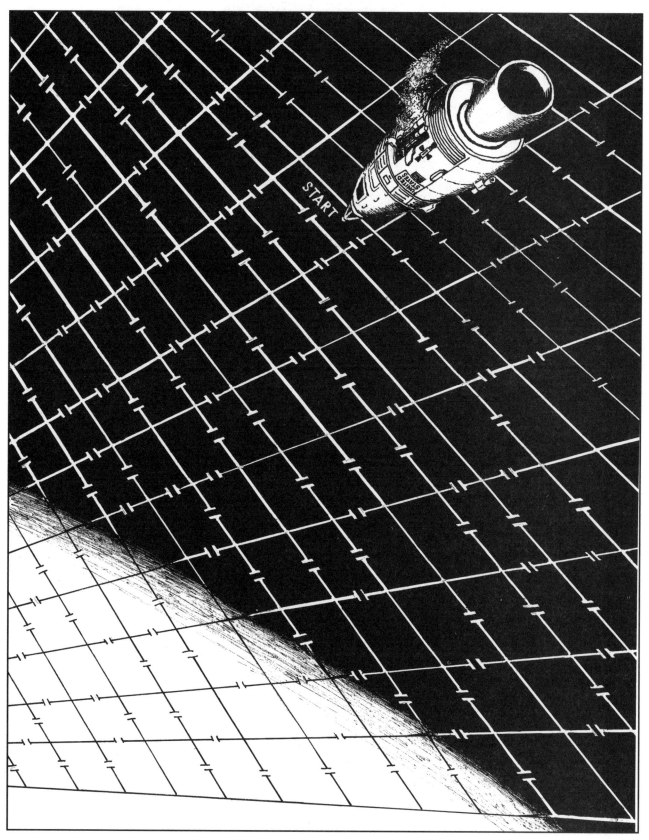

Crash in the Andes

In 1972, a plane crashed in the Andes Mountains with forty-five people on

START

board. Search efforts failed. Ten weeks after the crash, however, two survivors managed to hike out for help. Help them find their way by locating a clear path down the mountain.

Escape from Alcatraz

Because of strong currents around the prison at Alcatraz Island in San Francisco

SUCCESSFUL LANDING HERE

Bay, it has always been believed that no one could ever escape. Some tried and were never heard from again. Did they succeed? Put it to the test. Can you escape by swimming to shore?

Escape from Devil's Island

In French Guiana, in South America, there is an island prison known as Devil's

Island. You might be able to get away from this escape-proof island if you reached the coast and jumped into the sea. There you could attempt to swim to freedom. Find a clear path to the coast.

Sudden Death on Everest

In 1996, after a violent storm, Beck Weathers was given up for dead 300 yards from camp. Next morning, he woke alive. Help him find a clear path to his camp.

Helicopter Rescue on Everest

Beck's camp is too high for helicopter rescue. He is very weak and you only have two days to get him down to where the helicopter can make a daring try to save him.

CONGRATULATIONS

The men who actually lived through these escapes and rescues experienced a lot. There is no doubt about that. You've had the opportunity to follow them in all of their escapes, and even though your efforts were not physically demanding and did not carry the same risks, you still had to muster up the determination and courage to face and complete each situation. You never quit or gave up, even though the going might have been tough at times. Chances are, as a product of your experiences with these great escapes, you probably will be better prepared to face your need to escape should that circumstance ever occur.

If you had any trouble with the mazes in this book or would like to check your work, refer to the following guides for their solutions.

Escape from the *Titanic*

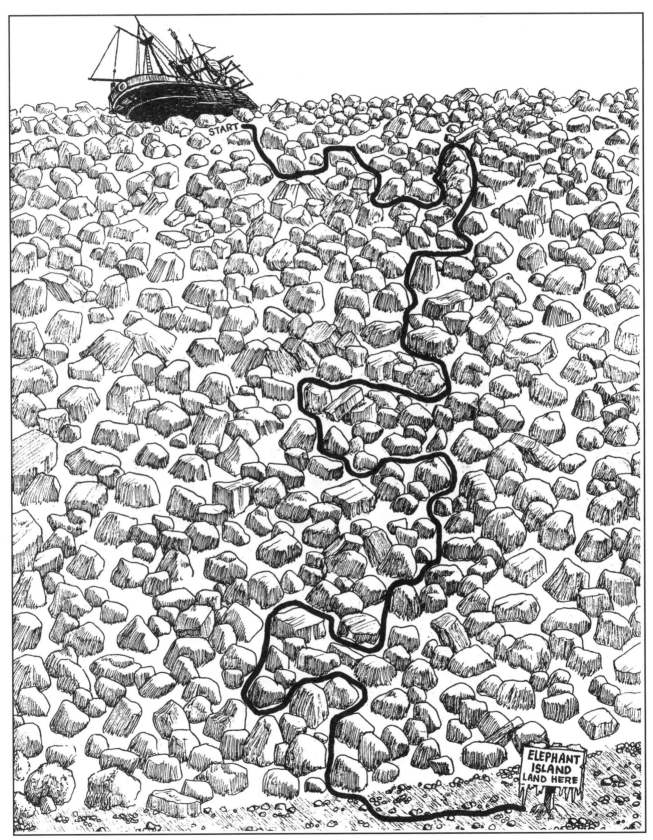

Go for Help for the Stranded Crew

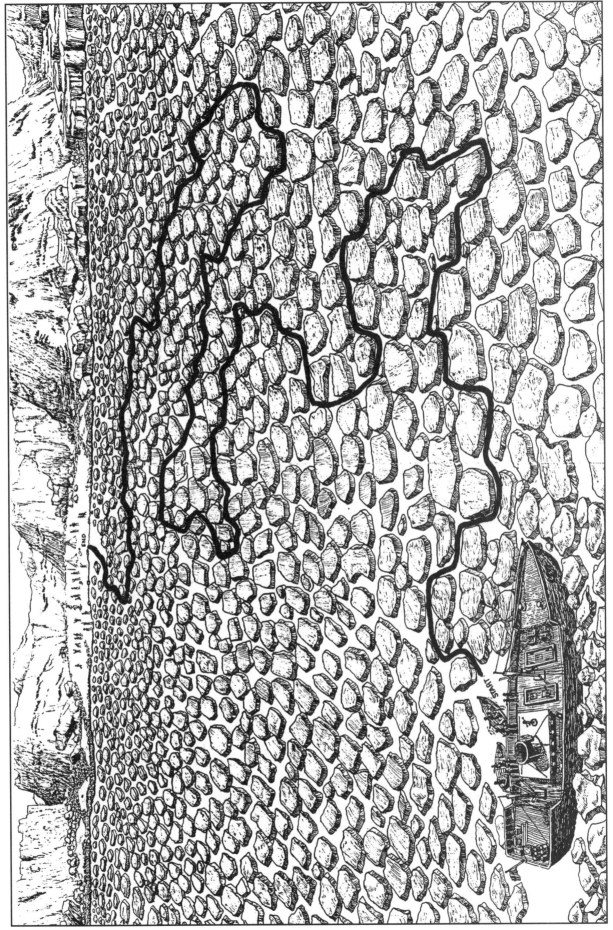

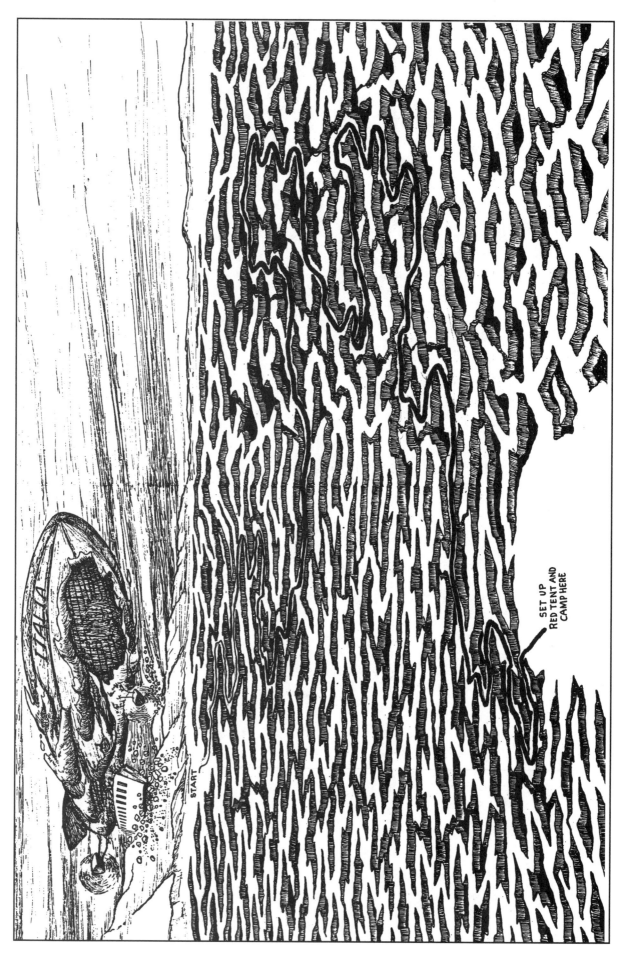

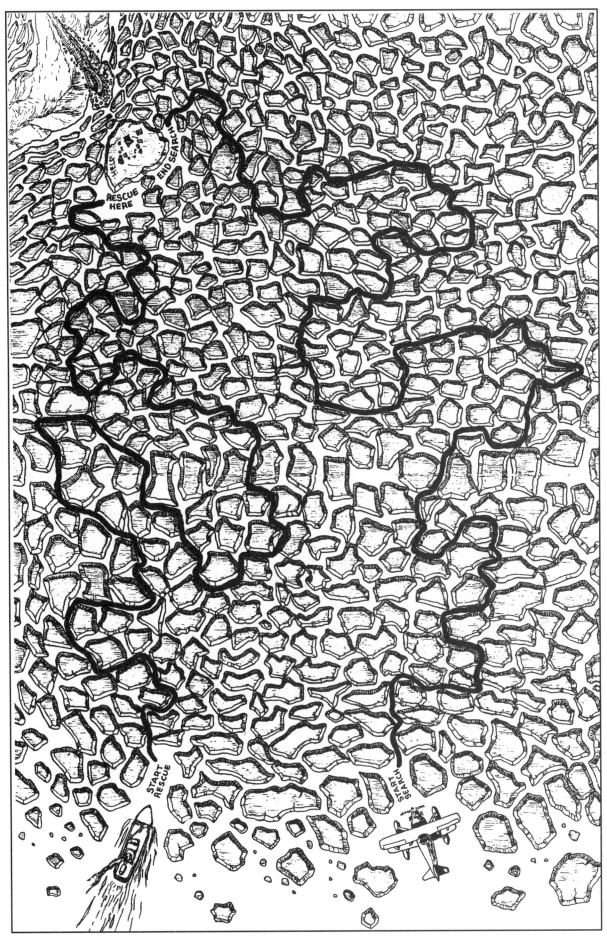

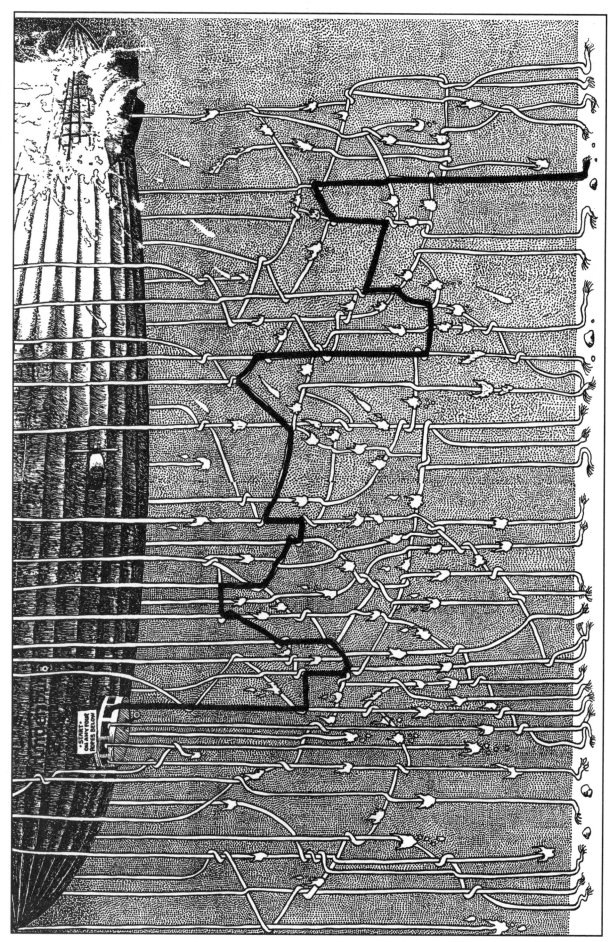

The *Squalus Is Down*

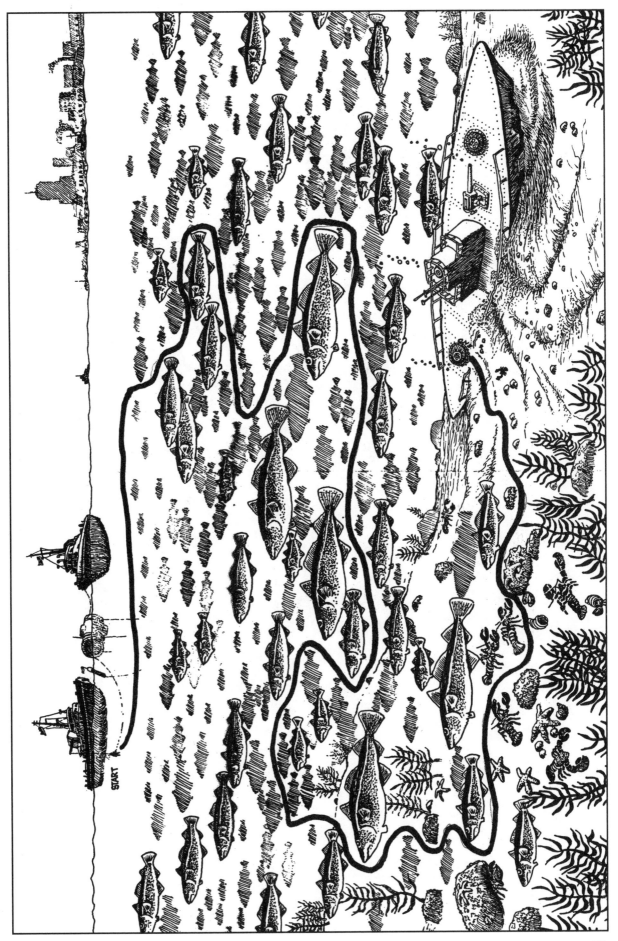

START

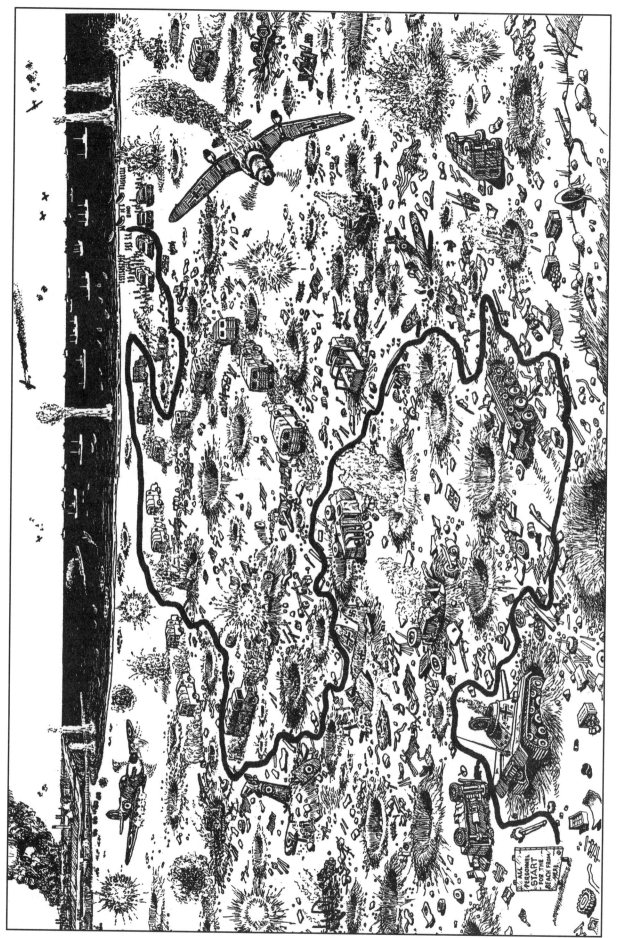

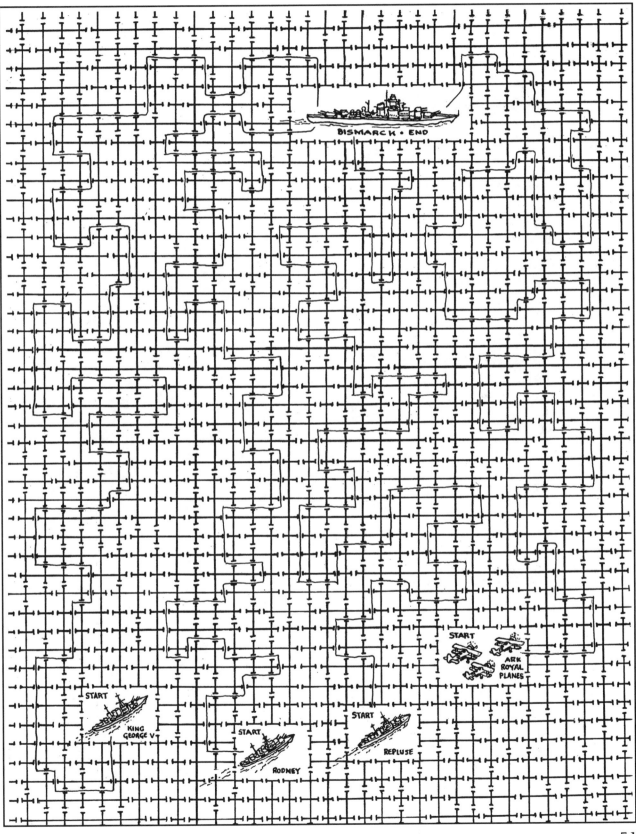

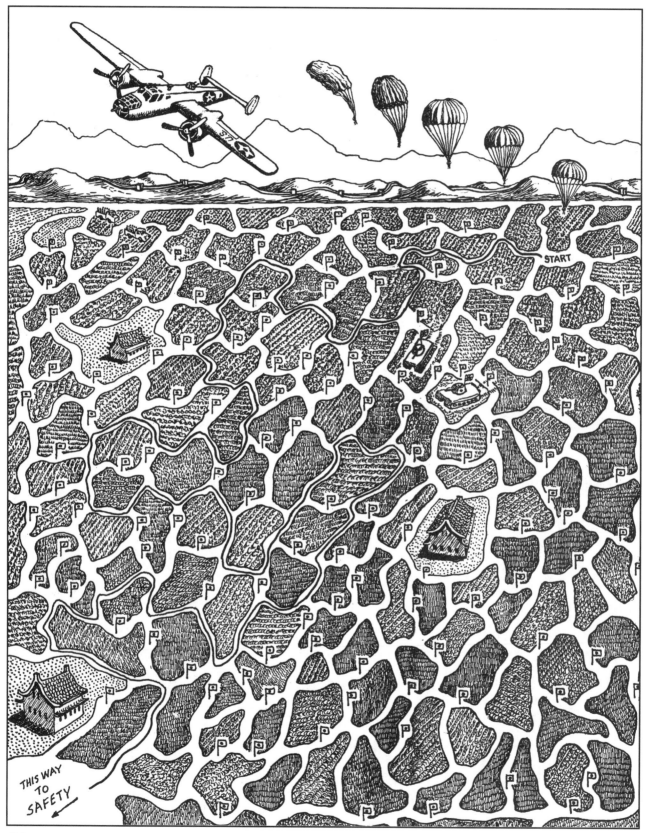

The Great Escape

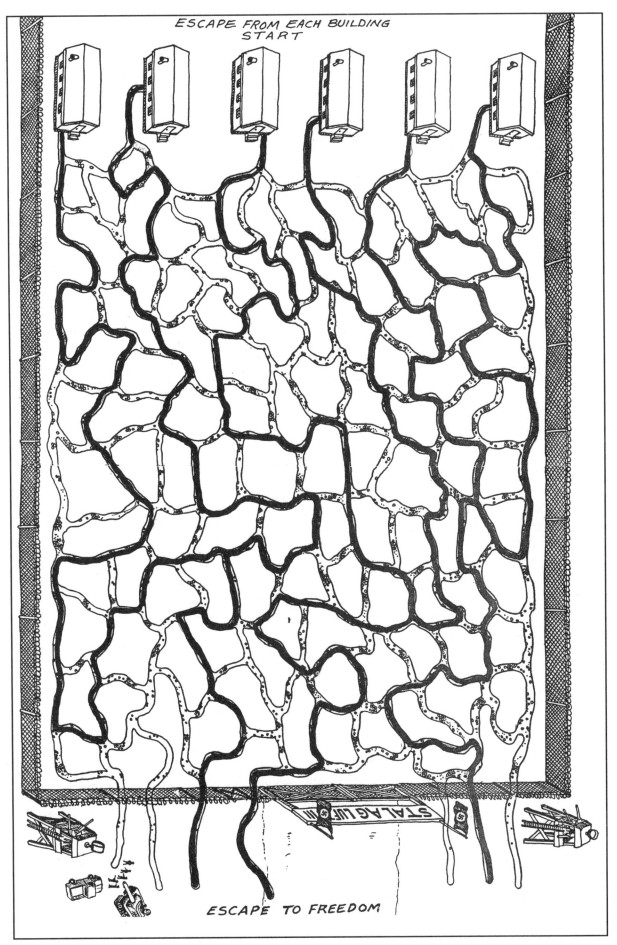

ESCAPE FROM EACH BUILDING
START

ESCAPE TO FREEDOM

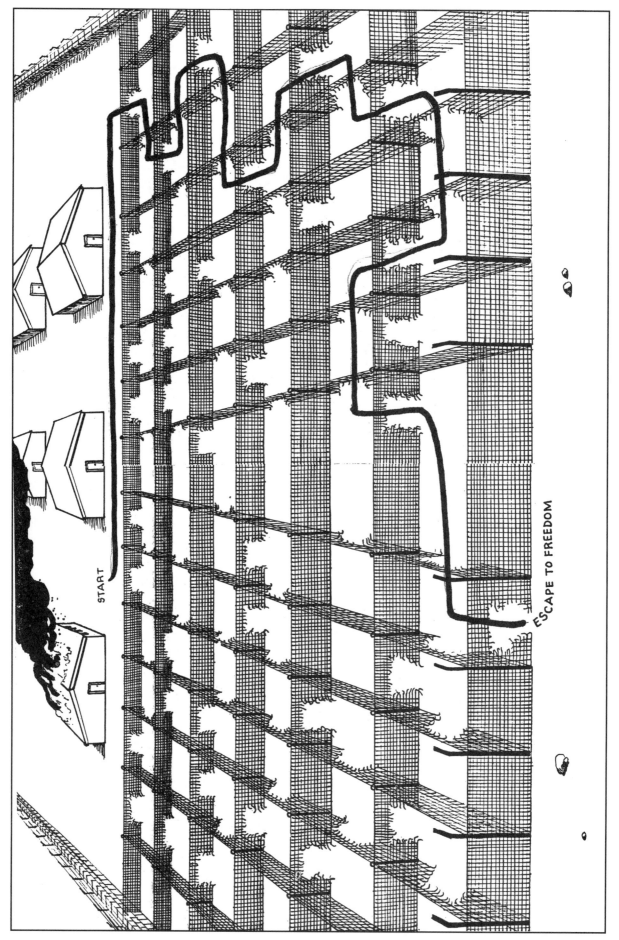

Escape from Sobibor

START

ESCAPE TO FREEDOM

MacArthur Must Flee Corregidor

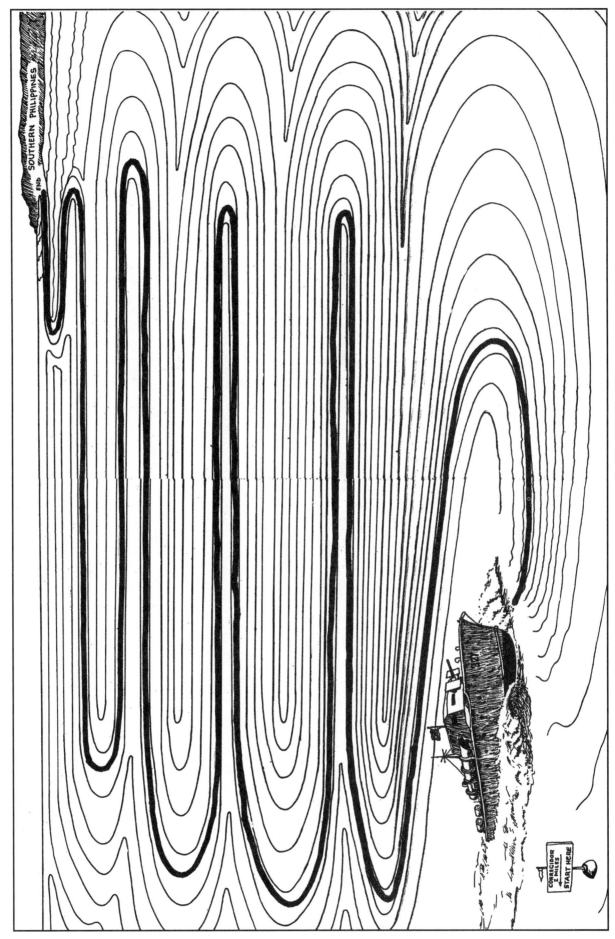

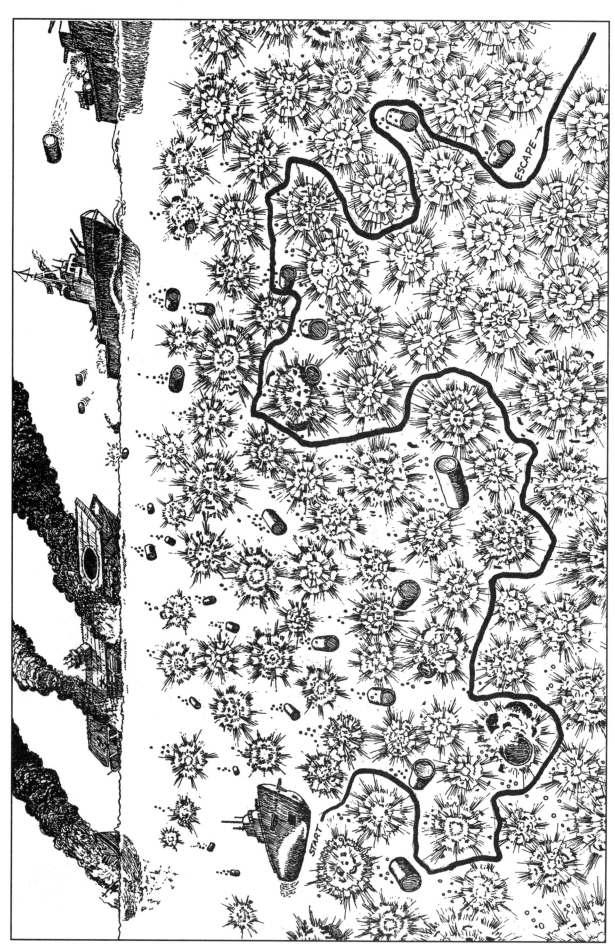

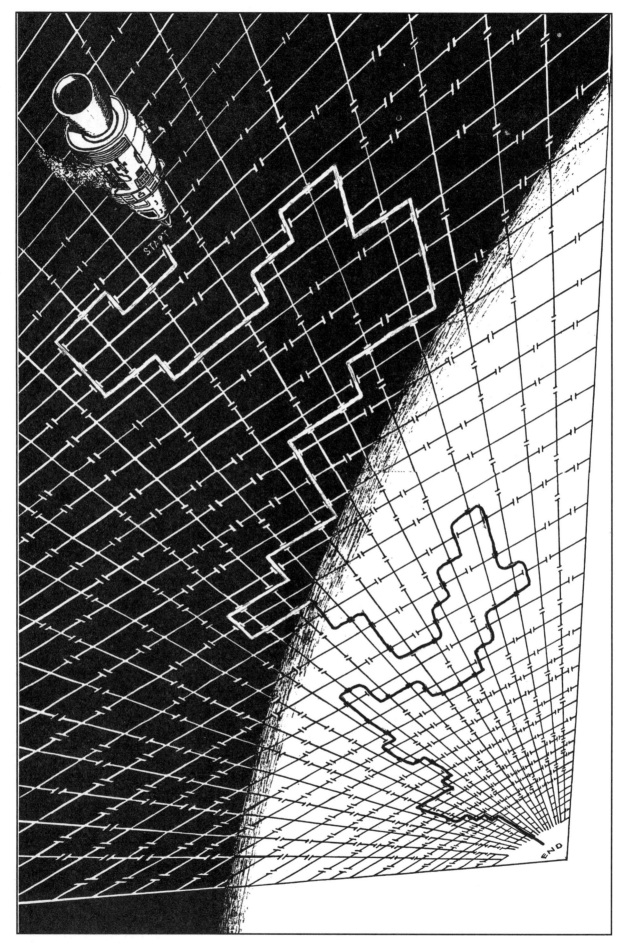

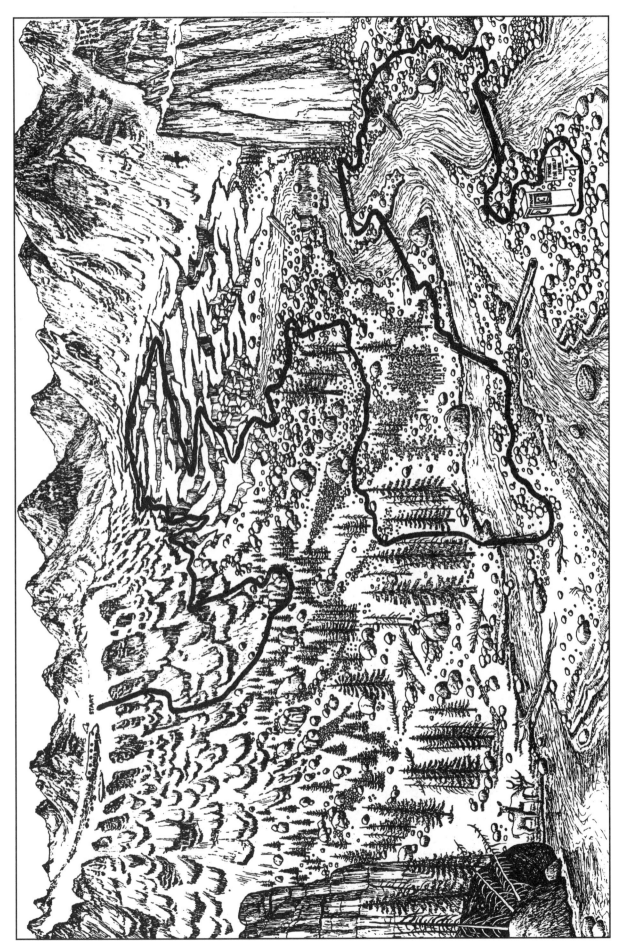

Escape from Alcatraz

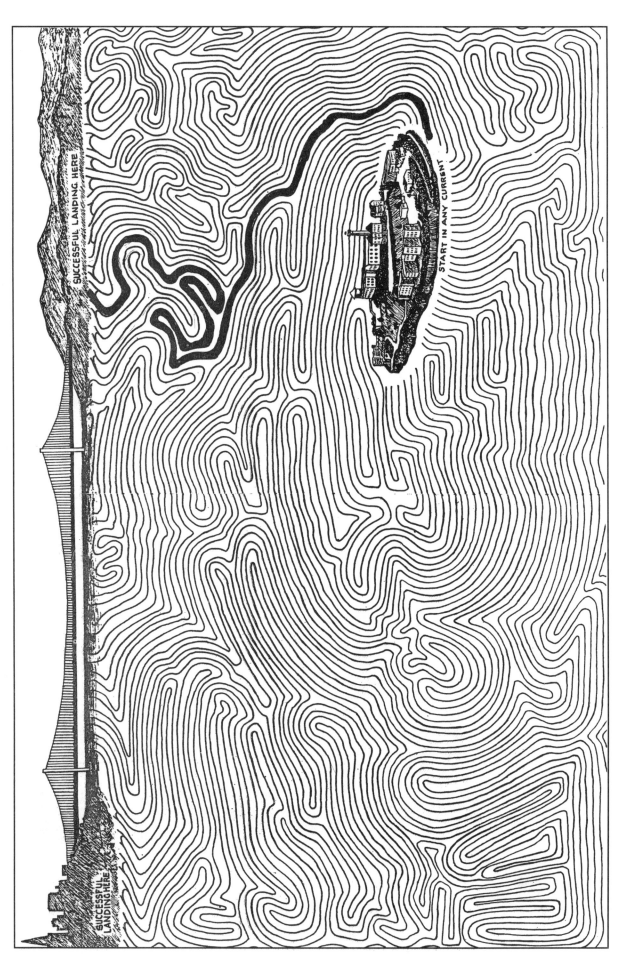

60

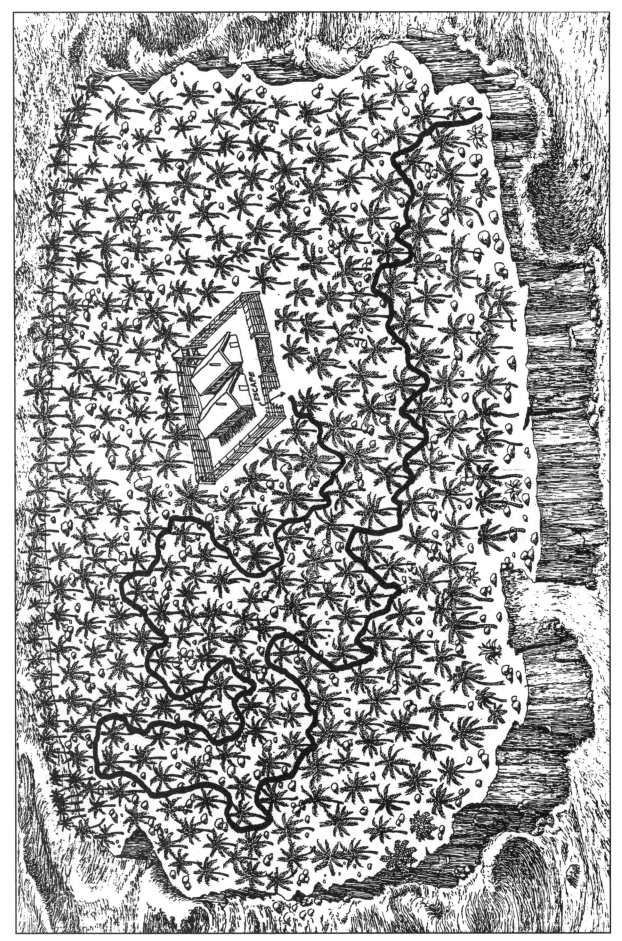

ESCAPE

Sudden Death on Everest

Index

Escape guides are noted in italics